A Nest for the Savior

AN INTERACTIVE
CHRISTMAS TRADITION

WRITTEN BY DIDI ZAYAS
ILLUSTRATED BY DEJA SESSA

ANTIQUE
AT HEART
PRESS

For Theodore, Audrey, Miles, and Jude.
You make the adventure sweet.
—D.Z.

To Sky, Remy, and Jory,
who taught me perseverance
beyond what I thought possible
while I illustrated this book.

—D.S.

ISBN 978-1-7325826-0-6

Text Copyright © 2018 Didi Zayas.
Illustration Copyright © 2018 Deja Sessa.

Visit www.AntiqueAtHeart.com and www.ANestForTheSavior.com.
First edition, October 2018

Publisher's Cataloging-in-Publication data

Names: Zayas, Didi, author. | Sessa, Deja, illustrator.
Title: A Nest for the Savior : an interactive Christmas tradition / written by Didi Zayas ; illustrated by Deja
Sessa.
Description: Plantation, FL: Antique at Heart Press, 2018.
Identifiers: ISBN 978-1-7325826-0-6 | 978-1-7325826-1-3
Summary: An inspirational retelling of the first Christmas story and a companion Advent activity guide.
Subjects: LCSH Christmas—Juvenile fiction. | Advent—Juvenile fiction. | Jesus Christ—Juvenile fiction. |
Birds—Nests—Juvenile fiction. | BISAC JUVENILE FICTION—Holidays & Celebrations—Christmas &
Advent.
Classification: LCC PZ7 .Z29 Ne 2018| DDC [E]—dc23

Each year, as the temperature drops with the last autumn leaf, the story of the first Christmas echoes around the world.

But very few have heard the whole story …

This is Sadie's
side of the story.

Sadie thought she was just an ordinary
sparrow, meant for nothing more than
weaving nests and humming lullabies.

But, often, she dreamt of adventure.
In fact, she was snoozing peacefully
in the sycamore branches, when . . .

Whoosh!

A trumpet's blast knocked her from her nest!

A light filled the sky and
an angel appeared, proclaiming:
"Today, the Savior has been born.
You'll know it's Him when you find
a baby in a barn, sleeping in a manger!"

"The ancient stories about the Savior are true!"
Sadie got goosebumps. "I bet I can find Him
before these shepherds!"

As the men prepared for their journey,
the curious sparrow was already
soaring above Bethlehem.

Soon, she heard a faint
coo rising from a stable.

Perched in the window,
Sadie saw the Savior
swaddled close to
His mother.

*This has to be Him!
I can feel it in my
feathers,* she thought.

But the manger was completely empty!

"OH, NO!"

Sadie was worried.

"The angel told the shepherds to look for a baby sleeping in a manger. I don't want them to miss Him!"

"I need to build a nest for the Savior!"

From the window, Sadie
swiftly called for help:

"Finally! At last, the
Savior is here!

Please rush to His side
with gifts and good cheer.

For God's Holy One has
no place to rest.

And I'm on a quest to
build Him a nest!"

First, a horse and three chickens answered the call with patches of hay and bits of pine. A donkey followed, offering his old, frayed rope, while a colony of ants marched in with a mountain of ribbon.

Sadie wrapped up their presents, but
the manger was still rather bare.

"We need more help!" she cried,
dashing off to share the news
through the forest.

"Finally! At last, the
Savior is here!

Please rush to His side
with gifts and good cheer.

For God's Holy One has
no place to rest.

And I'm on a quest to
build Him a nest!"

A goat and a deer sprang forth from the woods with bits of bread and blossoms of scarlet.

A lion cub pounced in next, offering scraps of linen, followed by a pair of doves with olive branches in their beaks.

"Hurry to town!" Sadie chirped, though
she feared their gifts would not be enough.

"I wish I had a gift for the
Savior, but all I own is my
simple, brown nest."

That gave her an idea.

She rushed home, crooning across the fields:

"Finally! At last, the Savior is here!
Please rush to His side with gifts and good cheer.
For God's Holy One has no place to rest.
And I'm on a quest to build Him a nest!"

As Sadie gathered her gift, a lamb, a cow and a duck arrived with tufts of wool, long, soft grasses, and downy feathers. "Quick! Follow me!" Sadie crowed.

When they reached the stable, the Savior was surrounded by her new friends.

Sadie quickly knit their items together and crowned the manger with a gift of her own.

At last, the Savior's mother gently
laid down her sleeping babe.

Just then, sandals scuffled outside.

The shepherds were in awe!
Everything was just as the angel had promised.
"This must be the Messiah!" they exclaimed.
The creatures cheered for their
Savior and for Sadie!

As for her nest, Sadie no longer needed it.

She followed Jesus from that day on.

And she had quite an adventure.

Flip the book to make a nest for your Savior.

Flip the book to read Sadie's story.

ABOUT THE AUTHOR & ILLUSTRATOR

Author Didi Zayas created A Nest for the Savior to help families connect—with their Savior and one another—during the busy Christmas season. She lives in South Florida, with her husband and four children, where she spends her time homeschooling her kids, listening to Christmas music and visiting her favorite places, EPCOT and Chick-fil-A. In addition to children's books, Didi creates educational games for children, which are available at AntiqueAtHeart.com.

Illustrator Deja Sessa is a Florida-transplant living in Fort Worth, Texas, with her husband, three daughters, two goats, seven chickens, two dogs, and two cats. Aside from her family, she is passionate about Jesus, homesteading, homeschooling, home birth, immunological science, and finding the art in it all. Her favorite part about creating the artwork for A Nest for the Savior was getting to serve God through her passion for art. To see more of her work, please visit Instagram.com/deesessart.

SHARE YOUR NEST FOR THE SAVIOR!

Share a photo of your nest with us using @ANestForTheSavior. Post your photo with #BestNestContest for a chance to win prizes!

Sharing your nest is also a great way to share the Good News about your Savior with friends and family this Christmas.

SHOW US WHAT YOU MADE WITH:

@ANestForTheSavior
#ANestForTheSavior
#BestNestContest

For more ideas, free downloads, and official contest rules, visit ANestForTheSavior.com.

GIVE HIM YOUR BEST

THE FINAL STEP

The Savior & The Story
Symbols of God's Plan for Us

Add your illustration of Jesus to your nest.

Now you know the whole story!

Our Savior was born on Christmas, so He could die for our sins on Good Friday. But He didn't stay in the tomb. On Easter, he rose again, and someday He will bring us to our eternal home in heaven with Him. And that is the wonderful reason we celebrate Christmas! But there's one final step! At last! It's time! Place the Savior in your nest! Sadie may have been just an ordinary sparrow, but God loves to use ordinary people for His extraordinary plans. Before she met Jesus, Sadie thought her only purpose was to build nests and sing lullabies. But God used Sadie's "ordinary" gifts to give her the adventure of a lifetime! He let Sadie in on the secret of the Savior's birth—and she used the voice God gave her to tell the whole world about Jesus! As you place your Savior in the manger, think about the adventure you've had learning about the King of kings, the Prince of Peace, the Good Shepherd and the Bread of Life. When you get to know the Savior, it's easy to see how extraordinary He is—and how His love makes your life special too! Sadie knew the secret… and, now, you do too!

- *It is finished!* -

FOLLOW IN SADIE'S FOOTSTEPS

Your quest to build Jesus a nest is now complete! Sadie would be proud! But building the nest wasn't Sadie's greatest accomplishment. The best choice Sadie ever made was to follow Jesus. You can follow Jesus too! We may not walk in His actual footsteps like Sadie did, but Jesus gave us instructions we can follow every day in the Bible, God's Holy Word! Plus, He says if we believe in Him, we will have eternal life in heaven forever! Isn't that amazing? If you want to follow Jesus like Sadie, say a simple prayer like this:

Dear Jesus,

I love You, and I want to follow You. I have sinned, but I am so thankful that You died on the Cross and forgave me because You love me! Thank You for coming on Christmas Day so I could have eternal life in heaven with You. I will never forget that You make my life extraordinary! AMEN!

STEP 10 — The Cow & The Grass
Symbols of God's Loving Care

> Add grass or strips of green paper to your nest.

The cow brought Sadie grass from the field to remind us that God cares about us. Jesus said, "*Walk into the fields and look at the wildflowers. … Have you ever seen color and design quite like it? The ten best-dressed men and women in the country look shabby alongside them. If God gives such attention to the wildflowers, most of them never even seen, don't you think he'll attend to you, take pride in you, do his best for you?*" (Luke 12:27-28, MSG). God cares for the fields and the flowers even though they live for a few months at most, but He cares about you so much more! He loves you so much that He sent Jesus so you could be with Him forever! As you add grass to your nest, remember that God loves you and cares for you.

STEP 11 — The Duck & The Feathers
Symbols of God's Peace and Comfort

> Add feathers of any kind to your nest.

The duck's feathers must've softened up Jesus' nest nicely. Her cozy feathers represent the peace of God. We're all afraid from time to time, but the Bible says the Prince of Peace was "given" to us on Christmas Day. Isaiah 9:6 says, "*For to us a child is born, to us a son is given, and the government will be on his shoulders. And he will be called Wonderful Counselor, Mighty God, Everlasting Father, Prince of Peace*" (NIV). Can you imagine a world where Jesus is in charge? How would that world be different from the one we live in today? I bet it would be a much more peaceful place. The Bible says heaven is a lot like that! In heaven, nothing scary or sad exists, and the Prince of Peace is in charge. I can't wait to see that! As you fluff up your nest with feathers, thank God for giving you peace that will never end.

STEP 12 — The Sparrow & The Nest
Symbols of Our True Home

> Add a bird's nest—or a drawing of one—to the manger.

Sadie gave up everything she had when she gave Jesus her nest as a pillow. And, in return, God gave her an adventure and a home that will never go away. He is preparing a place for us in heaven, too! Jesus said, "*My Father's house has many rooms. … And if I go and prepare a place for you, I will come back and take you to be with me*" (John 14:2-4, NIV). I want a room in God's house someday, don't you? God cared for Sadie so much that He let her be a part of the very first Christmas story. But here's a secret: He cares for you more! Jesus said, "*Are not two sparrows sold for a penny? Yet not one of them will fall to the ground outside your Father's care. And the very hairs of your head are all numbered. So don't be afraid; you are worth more than many sparrows*" (Matthew 10:29-31, NIV). When you add your nest to the manger, think about how much Jesus loves you. He loves you even more than His own life!

STEP 7

The Lion & The Linen
Symbols of the Resurrection

Add pieces of white fabric or paper towels to your nest.

Lions can be frightening creatures. But in Revelation, Jesus is called the Lion of Judah. Does that mean Jesus is scary and ferocious? No way! It means He is a triumphant King just like lions are the kings of all wild beasts. After His crucifixion, Jesus was wrapped in linen from head to toe. But when His disciples returned to the tomb, the strips of linen were lying there, with no body to be found! It was one of the first signs of His resurrection! Acts 2:24 says this about Jesus: *"God raised him from the dead ... because it was impossible for death to keep its hold on him"* (NIV). Death couldn't beat Jesus, because He is triumphant and victorious like a lion! As you lay your strips of linen in the nest, think about Jesus, the powerful Lion of Judah!

STEP 8

The Doves & The Olive Branches
Symbols of Everlasting Life

Add leaves or small branches to your nest.

I bet you've heard the story of Noah and the Ark. After many long days at sea, Noah sent out a dove, and it returned with an olive branch in its beak. Noah and his family were overjoyed, because that green twig was a sign that life was returning to earth—so they could get off the boat soon. The fresh, green olive branches the doves brought Sadie also represent life—the eternal life we have in Jesus. The Bible says, *"For God so loved the world that he gave his one and only Son, that whoever believes in him shall not perish but have eternal life"* (John 3:16, NIV). Can you believe God loves you that much? Our Creator loved us so much that He sent His Son to die in our place so that we could live with Him forever. When you add your greenery to the nest, thank God for sending Jesus so you could have eternal life!

STEP 9

The Lamb & The Wool
Symbols of the Savior's Sacrifice

Add cotton balls, stuffing, or wool to your nest.

The lamb gave Jesus her soft, fluffy wool. Before Jesus went to the Cross, people would sacrifice lambs when they sinned. But, Jesus paid for our sin completely when He died on the Cross. That's why He's called *"the Lamb of God, who takes away the sins of the world"* (John 1:29, NIV). He's also known as the Good Shepherd. In John 10:14-15, Jesus said, *"I know my sheep and my sheep know me . . . and I lay down my life for the sheep."* Isn't it amazing that Jesus knows all about us, even our flaws, and He still chose to sacrifice Himself for us? He must love us a lot! Isaiah 53:5 says that *"the punishment that brought us peace was on him, and by his wounds we are healed"* (NIV). As you add wool to your nest, remember the Lamb of God who took away our sins and the Good Shepherd who gave up His life for us, His sheep.

STEP 4

The Ants & The Gold Ribbon
Symbols of the King of kings

Add gold ribbon or strips of gold wrapping paper to your nest.

Next, the ants marched in with a mountain of gold ribbon. They chose royal gold because God is the King of kings! Proverbs 6:6-8 says, "*Take a lesson from the ants. … Though they have no prince or governor or ruler to make them work, they labor hard all summer, gathering food for the winter*" (NLT). Ants are hard workers. They can even lift items 5,000 times their own body weight! That sounds like they can lift mountains to me! With Jesus, we can move mountains too! Jesus said, "*Truly I tell you, if you have faith as small as a mustard seed, you can say to this mountain, 'Move from here to there,' and it will move. Nothing will be impossible for you*" (Matthew 17:20, NIV). A mustard seed is tiny like an ant. So, Jesus was saying that with just a little faith, we can move mountains! When you add your gold ribbon to the nest, remember the King of kings who gives us the power to move mountains!

STEP 5

The Goat & The Bread
Symbols of the Bread of Life

Add pieces of bread, sponge, or foam to your nest.

Goats are funny little creatures, aren't they? They will eat almost anything! But, Sadie's friend sacrificed his bread for Jesus instead. He must've known that bread represents Jesus in many ways! In fact, Jesus said, "*I am the bread of life. Whoever comes to me will never go hungry, and whoever believes in me will never be thirsty*" (John 6:35, NIV). Jesus meant that He will meet our every need. You need things like food, water, clothing, and shelter to survive, and your caregivers provide them for you. And if God loves you even more than they do, imagine what blessings are in store for you! Jesus promises to meet our every need. As you fill your manger with bread, think about how God provides for you!

STEP 6

The Deer & The Scarlet Blossoms
Symbols of Our Sin

Add red flowers or petals to your nest.

The deer brought Sadie blossoms of scarlet, which is just a fancy word for "deep red." The deer's red flowers represent our sins, whatever they may be. Think about one of your sins. We've all done something we wish we could take back. In Isaiah 1:18, the Bible says, "*Though your sins are like scarlet, they shall be as white as snow*" (NIV). Did you hear that verse? The sin you just thought of is now "as white as snow" because of Jesus! That means your sin is erased! Isn't that an awesome reason to celebrate Him this Christmas? When you fill your nest with scarlet flowers, thank God for forgiving you!

STEP 1

The Horse & The Hay
Symbols of Our True Strength

Add a handful of hay or Easter basket grass to your nest.

Sadie's friend the horse was the first animal to give a gift to the Savior. Sadie probably thought that he was much stronger than she was, but Sadie's strength came from trusting in God. The Bible says, *"Some trust in chariots and some in horses, but we trust in the name of the LORD our God"* (Psalm 20:7, NIV). Sadie's friend had very strong muscles, yet he couldn't fill the manger on his own. But, God's strength is limitless. With His help, small, little Sadie filled the entire manger. In Matthew 19:26, Jesus said, *"With man this is impossible, but with God all things are possible"* (NIV). When you add hay to the manger, remember that real strength comes from trusting in Jesus!

STEP 2

The Chickens & The Pine
Symbols of the Cross

Add twigs from the yard, wood shavings, or brown shreds of paper to your nest.

The chickens brought Jesus soft pieces of pine from their coop. The wood shavings represent the wooden cross, where Jesus gave up His life for us. Romans 5:8 says, *"God demonstrates his own love for us in this: While we were still sinners, Christ died for us"* (NIV). When we celebrate Christmas, we need to remember the real reason Jesus came: for the Cross. We celebrate His birth because He was willing to die for us. He was born in the stable and placed in the manger because He had a holy purpose—to be nailed to a sinner's Cross in our place. Without the Cross, we wouldn't have a relationship with God or a chance to go to heaven. Then Christmas wouldn't be much of a celebration, would it? As you add bits of pine to the nest, think about the Cross—the real reason for the season.

STEP 3

The Donkey & The Rope
Symbols of Freedom

Add pieces of rope, yarn or string to your nest.

The donkey wanted to see the Savior so badly that he broke free from the ropes holding him back. Imagine if you were tied up every day like the donkey. That doesn't sound like fun, does it? But there's good news! One of the reasons Jesus came on Christmas was to set us all free! Jesus said, *"The Spirit of the Lord is on me, because he has anointed me to proclaim good news to the poor. He has sent me to proclaim freedom for the prisoners and recovery of sight for the blind . . ."* (Luke 4:18-19, NIV). Our sins are like the donkey's rope—they hold us back from God's blessings and eternal life. But Jesus broke the chains of sin on the Cross to set us free! As you lay your rope in the nest, thank God for setting you free.

Prepare your heart for the Savior

Read Luke Chapter 2:1-20 aloud

"In those days Caesar Augustus issued a decree that a census should be taken of the entire Roman world. … And everyone went to their own town to register.

So Joseph also went up from the town of Nazareth in Galilee to Judea, to Bethlehem the town of David, because he belonged to the house and line of David. He went there to register with Mary, who was pledged to be married to him and was expecting a child. While they were there, the time came for the baby to be born, and she gave birth to her firstborn, a son. She wrapped him in cloths and placed him in a manger, because there was no guest room available for them.

And there were shepherds living out in the fields nearby, keeping watch over their flocks at night. An angel of the Lord appeared to them, and the glory of the Lord shone around them, and they were terrified. But the angel said to them, 'Do not be afraid. I bring you good news that will cause great joy for all the people. Today in the town of David a Savior has been born to you; he is the Messiah, the Lord. This will be a sign to you: You will find a baby wrapped in cloths and lying in a manger.'

Suddenly a great company of the heavenly host appeared with the angel, praising God and saying, 'Glory to God in the highest heaven, and on earth peace to those on whom his favor rests.'

When the angels had left them and gone into heaven, the shepherds said to one another, 'Let's go to Bethlehem and see this thing that has happened, which the Lord has told us about.'

So they hurried off and found Mary and Joseph, and the baby, who was lying in the manger. When they had seen him, they spread the word concerning what had been told them about this child, and all who heard it were amazed at what the shepherds said to them. But Mary treasured up all these things and pondered them in her heart. The shepherds returned, glorifying and praising God for all the things they had heard and seen, which were just as they had been told" (NIV).

Prepare for the adventure

copy or trace before coloring

CREATING THE NEST, THE SAVIOR & THE MANGER

You can make your nest for the Savior in one sitting or as a 12-day Advent activity to prepare your heart fo Christmas. As a daily activity, it's best to start Step 1 on December 13th if you want to add Jesus to the manger o Christmas Eve or on December 14th if you want to place Him in the manger on Christmas morning. To creat your illustration of the Savior, copy this page or download a copy from ANestForTheSavior.com. Then color an cut around the edges before you place Him in the manger. In biblical days, the manger was a long, deep containe used to feed farm animals. You may not have a manger lying around the house, but I bet you have a shoe box o a plastic bin you can use instead! If you're crafty, feel free to add to the illustration above. You can also cover you manger with brown paper or paint to make it look like real wood.

LET'S BUILD A NEST FOR THE SAVIOR!

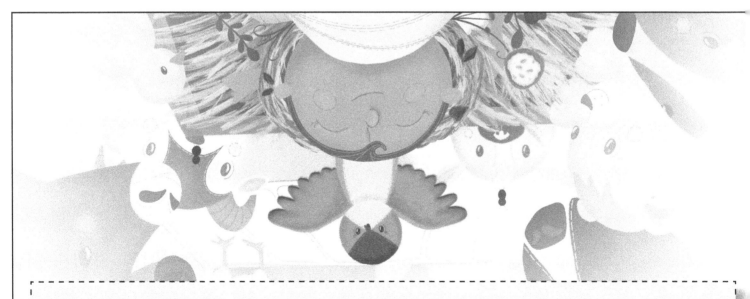

As we weave the items below together, we'll learn how Jesus fills our ordinary lives with extraordinary hope and adventure! All of the objects Sadie and her friends brought to the manger are symbolic. That means they can teach us about Jesus, the first Christmas, and the Cross!

Are you ready for an adventure? Great! Let's get to work.

What you need

These items can be found around the house, at a craft store or for sale in the Nest Activity Kit.

- 1 container to use as a manger
- 1 copy of the illustration of Jesus

- a handful of hay or Easter basket grass
- twigs, wood shavings or shreds of paper
- pieces of rope, yarn or string
- gold ribbon or strips of gold wrapping paper
- pieces of bread, sponge, or foam
- red flowers or petals

- pieces of white fabric or paper towels
- leaves or small branches
- cotton balls, stuffing, or wool
- grass or green strips of paper
- feathers of any kind
- a bird's nest or a drawing of one

The items above are simply suggestions. Feel free to substitute for similar items of your choice or draw a picture of an item if necessary. For ideas to create the items above, visit NestForTheSavior.com.

CPSIA information can be obtained
at www.ICGtesting.com
Printed in the USA
LVHW011804121120
671498LV00007B/124